LINWEAVE
LIMITED EDITIONS

MCMXXXI

THE LINWEAVE ASSOCIATION

Contents

FOREWORD   By Frederick Allen Williams   Pages 5-6

INTRODUCTION   By Wilbur Lewis   Pages 7-25

I   THE COURSE   By Daniel Chase

II   THE LUTE GIRL   By Po Chü-i

III   THE TIGER   By William Blake

IV   KUBLA KAHN   By Samuel Taylor Coleridge

V   AFTER BLENHEIM   By Robert Southey

VI   ABOU BEN ADHEM   By Leigh Hunt

VII   TO HELEN   By Edgar Allan Poe

VIII   NON SUM QUALIS ERAM BONAE
        SUB REGNO CYNARAE   By Ernest Dowson

IX   THE CONGO   By Vachel Lindsay

X   A BIRD IN A GILDED CAGE   By Arthur Lamb and
                                Harry Von Tilzer

Foreword

SOME eleven years ago a group of paper merchants conceived the idea of an association of merchants, manufacturers, and converters with the single purpose of developing a finer, more comprehensive line of book and announcement papers than any individual member could hope to produce. The name LINWEAVE was selected, and the group became the Linweave Association.

In the years that followed, continual research work applied to the manufacture of paper kept Linweave Papers right in step with the progress of printing and with the development of new printing equipment. With the world's sources to draw upon for the manufacture of fine papers, and with the facilities of the Kellogg Division of the U. S. Envelope Company for the converting of paper into envelopes to match, the Linweave organization has placed its name in the foremost rank of producers of fine papers.

Under the name LINWEAVE, printing papers are produced for the Association as a cooperative group. The benefit of the group's pooled experience in meeting the demands of printer, publisher, and advertising man is apparent in the fact that each new paper is developed to meet a definite market need. The elimination of many manufacturing and sales expenses enables the Association to build greater values into Linweave Papers than are found in papers produced under the old mill-to-merchant-to-consumer marketing methods.

In presenting Linweave Papers to our friends and customers, a new idea occurred to us early in 1930. Instead of following the usual custom of mailing out commercial samples to demonstrate types of printing for which Linweave papers were adapted, we decided to select a number of interesting short writings and to print them after the style of the fine Limited Edition books which are gaining such widespread popularity. Thus, in time, we would give our friends the Linweave Limited Editions—a beautiful collection of art work and printing from the finest presses of the United States, produced on Linweave Papers.

In carrying out this project we have been exceptionally fortunate in our contacts. Our first confidant to the plan was Wilbur Lewis of Springfield, Massachusetts, a Middle Westerner who reversed Horace Greeley's advice and came east to seek his fame and fortune. He was born in Cleveland, Ohio in 1904, and at an early age was transported even farther west where an education awaited him at the University of Missouri and in the business and editorial offices of the St. Louis Post Dispatch. Seven years ago, bitten with ambition, he headed for that Mecca of all writers—New York. There, until 1929, he spent his time winning recognition as a writer and as an advertising man in the intimate circles of New York's larger advertising agencies. The beauties of New England finally lured him to Springfield where as president of the firm of Lewis & Magee,

Inc. he was called upon to assist in the production of this volume. The hours he has spent alone in research and in writing the interesting introduction which follows, and the hours we have spent together in planning the contents have been very happy and very much worth while—and there have been far more hours devoted to this work than can be realized by its dimensions.

One of the first men contacted by Mr. Lewis and myself was Alexander King, the artist who illustrated The Congo. This was most fortunate, for he practically became art director for the series with no reward save the joy of helping to create some exceedingly beautiful printed pieces.

And so the work comes to an end and is herewith sincerely dedicated to our friends and customers by the following members of the Linweave Association:

SLOAN PAPER COMPANY, Atlanta, Ga., Birmingham, Ala.; THE BARTON, DUER & KOCH PAPER Co., Baltimore, Md., Washington, D.C.; STORRS & BEMENT CO., Boston, Mass., New Haven, Conn., Portland, Me., Providence, R. I.; THE ALLING & CORY COMPANY, Buffalo, N.Y., New York, N.Y., Pittsburgh, Pa., Rochester, N.Y.; CASKIE PAPER COMPANY, INC., Charlotte, N.C.; CHICAGO PAPER Co., Chicago, Ill.; SWIGART PAPER CO., Chicago, Ill.; THE STANDARD PAPER CO., Cincinnati, Ohio; THE MILLCRAFT PAPER COMPANY, Cleveland, Ohio, Toledo, Ohio; E. C. PALMER & CO., LTD., Dallas, Texas, Houston, Texas, New Orleans, La., Tampa, Fla.; WESTERN PAPER COMPANY, Denver, Colo., Fort Wayne, Ind., Omaha, Neb.; WESTERN NEWSPAPER UNION, Des Moines, Iowa, Fargo, N. D., Lincoln, Neb., Little Rock, Ark., Oklahoma City, Okla., Salt Lake City, Utah, Sioux City, Iowa, Wichita, Kansas; SEAMAN-PATRICK PAPER CO., Detroit, Mich.; ZELLERBACH PAPER COMPANY, Eugene, Ore., Fresno, Cal., Long Beach, Cal., Los Angeles, Cal., Oakland, Cal., Phoenix, Ariz., Portland, Ore., Reno, Nev., Sacramento, Cal., San Diego, Cal., San Francisco, Cal., San Jose, Cal., Seattle, Wash., Spokane, Wash., Stockton, Cal.; CARPENTER PAPER CO., Grand Rapids, Mich.; THE JOHN LESLIE PAPER CO., Great Falls, Mont., Minneapolis, Minn.; CRESCENT PAPER COMPANY, Indianapolis, Ind.; MIDWESTERN PAPER COMPANY, Kansas City, Mo.; THE STANDARD PAPER CO., Louisville, Ky.; THE E. A. BOUER COMPANY, Milwaukee, Wis.; TAYLOE PAPER CO., Memphis, Tenn.; ALLAN & GRAY, New York, N.Y.; BEEKMAN PAPER & CARD CO., INC., New York, N.Y.; D. L. WARD COMPANY, Philadelphia, Pa.; B. W. WILSON PAPER CO., Richmond, Va.; MACK-ELLIOTT PAPER Co., St. Louis, Mo.; THE NASSAU PAPER CO., St. Paul, Minn.; THE PAPER HOUSE OF NEW ENGLAND, Springfield, Mass.; W. J. GAGE & CO., LTD., Toronto, Canada.

In closing, we who have had active participation in the production of the Linweave Limited Editions for 1931 wish to extend grateful thanks to all the artists, typographers, printers, and paper manufacturers who have helped make the task so pleasant and successful. We have one great hope—that this demonstration may make possible greater receptibility for high standards in printing and fine printing papers.

F. A. W.
Springfield, Mass., Nov. 10, 1931

THE SELECTIONS CHOSEN FOR THE 1931 SERIES OF Linweave Limited Editions form a somewhat peculiar anthology. It is not a collection of the poetry of any one nation, nor of any one era. It is not a collection intended to point a general or specific trend in literature, thought, life, or manners. It embraces a fragment of modern American prose, three of the most enduring of English poetic masterpieces, two lesser bits of English verse, two poems from the pens of American poets, one lovely contribution from the early Chinese, and one sentimental ballad from our own melodious nineties. Such a miscellany is necessarily difficult of classification to one primarily interested in the subjects chosen. But to one whose first interest centers in the manner in which the subjects are treated, several classifications are possible.

The ten editions, first of all, constitute a striking and comprehensive collection of present-day American printing at its best. The ten printers (eleven, counting the very excellent printer who printed the title page and introduction in the bound book) whose work is herein represented, rank well up on anybody's list of contemporary craftsmen. As a group they belong to no one school of printers. Some of them are unrelenting classicists, some have gone beyond the tried and tested methods and boldly set about experimenting with the newer processes and modern types. Whatever the differences in their individual opinions and approaches, they share one goal in common—good printing—and workmen as faithful as these can almost unfailingly be counted upon to reach that common goal.

The variety of techniques which make these editions so valuable to the student of printing is again evident in the type faces and printing processes employed. In all, twenty different type faces have been used with almost faultless taste, and the letterpress has been augmented by the newer water color and offset processes to obtain desired effects and to demonstrate the wider scopes these new developments make possible.

The Linweave Limited Editions are again of value as a practical demonstration of fine modern book illustration. The work of the eleven artists included does not conform to any single standard. Neither do the artists themselves fall into any convenient group classification, except that they are all outstanding artists. A few of them have long been successful book illustrators. Two of them are ranking artists whose work has never before been reproduced (a fact likely to enhance the value of these editions as the years go by). Still others are successful commercial artists whose work offered sufficient promise to justify entrusting to them assignments in this series.

The Limited Editions possess additional virtue as a demonstration of the progress achieved in the manufacture of American machine-made papers. For here we have the work of the foremost artists and printers of our time beautifully reproduced on and complemented by truly inexpensive papers whose quality and finish compare very favorably with the lovely but costly hand-made papers of another generation. To those of us confronted with the preparation of fine printing at moderate cost this is welcome progress indeed!

[7]

To choose ten interesting subjects within the prescribed limitations, to correlate the work of eleven printers and eleven artists, to keep ahead of the tremendous detail attendant upon the use of eleven different papers, three processes, and twenty type faces, and to give the whole venture a unity of sorts, has been an exacting but extremely interesting task. But to give, in the short space of an introductory chapter, a critical analysis of all the work represented in the series is an out-and-out impossibility. Volumes could be and have been devoted to the lives and work of the authors, artists, designers, and printers whose work is included.

What can be done is to summarize briefly some of the interesting facts encountered in the preparation of each edition.

THE COURSE
by Daniel Chase, *illustrated by* John Burlin
printed by D. B. Updike *at the Merrymount Press*
on Linweave Milano, White Jade

Shortly after his graduation from Dartmouth in 1914 Daniel Chase went to war. From the war he brought home a record and an ambition. The record: distinguished service with the Royal Air Force, "largely," he says, "in keeping the fire going in the mess bar against what time the lads returned from midnight egg-dropping on Mannheim." The ambition: to settle down and write and lead a quiet bachelor's life in the small New England village of Holliston, Massachusetts. He has published five novels, *Flood Tide* (written before the war), *The Middle Passage, Hardy Rye, Pines of Jalaam, Backfire,* and a number of short stories and articles for periodicals. By his own admission his outlook on life has mellowed considerably since 1922, when at the age of 32 he wrote *The Middle Passage,* a novel inspired by an old English ballad of anonymous origin, *Sir Patrick Spens.* Be that as it may, the words of Reece, first mate of the *Juno,* lifted almost bodily from the text to serve as introduction to the book, still remain a vivid and beautiful prose exposition of one very definite philosophy of life. Mr. Chase titled his introduction, *The Course*—the title under which it has been placed as an appropriate first edition for this book.

Born in Minnesota of a Swiss father and an Irish mother, John Burlin has made his life a happy, busy and profitable one. You may have cheered and thrilled at the hair-raising serials he used to direct for the old Essanay Company; in your travels you may have journeyed over some of the bridges he helps build in his role of construction engineer; if you have traveled at all in South America, he may easily have been a casual fellow passenger on train or boat. His longest stay in South America found him on a four-year expedition through Brazil and Peru, digging up additions for his splendid collection of Inca relics. Today, at 40, John Burlin is a millionaire, and a painter of note who paints solely for his own pleasure. He exhibits spasmodically, and his illustrations for *The Course* are the first he has made for reproduction.

Upon entering Daniel Berkeley Updike's office on the top floor of an up-to-date printing crafts building on Summer Street, you pass from the noise and bustle of modern Boston into the quiet and dignified atmosphere you associate with a New England of other days, the days of fine and careful craftsmanship, of clipper ships and India Wharf. If your imagination is vivid, you can catch the smell of the sea, the fragrance of tea leaves and spices, drifting through the open windows on a lazy spring afternoon. A step beyond the general office is Mr. Updike's real workroom, a library whose shelves are richly stocked with an unbelievably complete collection of fine editions, both American and European, both of the past and of the present. Instinctively you feel you have entered a sacred place, a temple mellow with memories of the pleasant meetings held within its doors, a Mecca for the lovers of fine printing who come to pay tribute to the genius of D. B. Updike. And though you may question the significance of these impressions, there can be no question as to the genius of Mr. Updike's work. Most consistent of all American printers, Mr. Updike has been a powerful leader in the renaissance of fine printing in this country. In last spring's exhibition of Fifty Books of 1931, selected for merit by the American Institute of Graphic Arts, were to be found six books bearing the impress of D. B. Updike and the Merrymount Press, a distinction bestowed on no other printer. In addition to the countless fine volumes he has printed, Mr. Updike has also written two books well worth your attention, *Printing Types, Their History, Forms and Use* and *In the Day's Work*.

For the typography of *The Course*, Mr. Updike chose hand set Janson Old Style, a type face cut by a seventeenth century type cutter of that name, and one for which he seems to have particular affection. The illustrations are reproduced from zinc line plates.

Linweave Milano, on which *The Course* is printed, closely resembles in texture and color the Ingres type of imported papers, yet it is machine-made at surprisingly moderate cost. White Jade, one of the five colors in which Milano is available, is an off-white which gives distinction and a deep rich background to the work of printer and illustrator.

THE LUTE GIRL

by Po Chü-i, *illustrated by* Victor Helleu
designed and printed by William A. Kittredge *at the Lakeside Press*
on Linweave Japan, Ivory, Antique

Fully a thousand years before Shelley, Byron, Keats, and the Lake Poets brought about the celebrated renaissance of English poetry, China entered upon a Golden Age of Poetry all her own. The years 618 to 906 embraced the reign of the famous T'ang dynasty, a line of emperors more devoted to the arts than to the guidance of the ship of state. Under their sympathetic patronage, China produced the three great poets, Li Po, Tu Fu, and Po Chü-i—the latter a statesman as well as a poet. On one occasion Po Chü-i incurred imperial disfavor, unfortunately for Po Chü-i but fortunately for the cause of poetry, for it was during his temporary banishment from court that he composed *The Lute Girl*, one of the most enduring masterpieces left to posterity by the Chinese poets. The origin of the poem, as told in Po Chü-i's own preface, is of interest:

"When after ten years of regular service," he writes, "I was wrongfully dismissed from the Prefecture of the Nine Rivers and the Mastership of the House, in the bright autumn of the year I was sent away to Ko-pen Creek's mouth. It was there that I heard, seated in my boat at midnight, the faint tones of a lute. It seemed as though I was listening to the tones of the gongs in the Palace of the Capital. On asking an old man, I learned that it was the performance of a woman who for many years had cultivated the two talents of music and singing to good effect. In the course of time, her beauty faded, she humbled her pride, and followed her fate by becoming a merchant's wife.

"The wine ran out and the songs ceased. My grief was such that I made a few short poems to set to music for singing.

"But now perturbed, engulfed, distressed, worn out, I move about the river and lake at my leisure. I have been out of office for two years, but the effect of this man's words is such as to produce a peaceful influence within me.

"This evening I feel that I have dismissed all the reproachful thoughts I harbored, and in consequence have made a long poem which I intend to present to the court."

The English versions of Po Chü-i's preface and the poem itself are translations by L. Cranmer-Byng and are taken from his lovely volume of Oriental translations, *Lute of Jade*. Cranmer-Byng was identified with the English literary movement of the early nineties (of which you shall hear more later in this introduction) and devoted himself to popularizing the poetry of the East.

In 1870, two years before the advent of Cranmer-Byng, Victor Helleu was born in Tours, France. Remaining there scarcely long enough to get his bearings, he set sail as a youth for the Orient, where he spent many years absorbing Oriental folklore and legend. He returned to design the Madame Butterfly setting for L'Opéra Français, and to illustrate a superb edition of his friend Pierre Loti's novel, *Madame Chrysanthème*. Before 1915 most of the children's books from France were embellished by his charming conceptions, but in that year he illustrated Lafcadio Hearn's Japanese fairy tales and put away his palette for keeps. Now he migrates from France to America (where his son prospers in business) and back again, constantly alert for duelling pistols of every variety to add to his already enviable collection. Only by extreme good fortune was he persuaded to leave his retirement long enough to illustrate *The Lute Girl*.

William A. Kittredge used Sylvan for his titles, and Fournier for his body type; he printed *The Lute Girl* entirely by the offset process, using two colors for type and borders, and seven colors for the illustration. So much is easy. But the manner in which he reproduced poem and illustration without losing one bit of the magic of the originals can only be ascribed to the unfailing skill and good taste which have rapidly placed Kittredge and his Lakeside Press high in the first flight of American printers. Born at Lowell, Massachusetts, in 1891, his first thought on entering the business world was for printing, and he has been at it ever since. Four years ago R. R. Donnelley & Sons realized his ability and set up for him The Lakeside Press which promptly began increasing America's output of fine editions. The original Rockwell Kent *Moby Dick* is a notable example. Now Mr. Kittredge has one more feather in his cap, for his *Lute Girl* was the folder chosen from the ten Linweave Limited Editions for display by the American Institute of Graphic Arts in its 1931 Printing for Commerce exhibition.

A more happy choice of paper for *The Lute Girl* can scarcely be imagined than Linweave Japan, whose delicate ivory shading so definitely enhances the beauty of the finished folder.

[10]

Linweave Japan is an unusual sheet—it possesses the parchment-like finish, the beauty, the soft colorings of Japanese vellums, yet it also has a uniform printing surface, uniform thickness, and is very moderately priced! To a printer familiar with Japan type papers this may be an unbelievable paradox, but it is true. As for the printing quality of Linweave Japan, well —look at *The Lute Girl.*

THE TIGER
by WILLIAM BLAKE, *illustrated by* THEODORE ROSS
designed and printed by CARL J. H. ANDERSON *at The Franklin Printing Company*
on Linweave Text, White, Antique

BORN into the Classical Age in England, when imagination was dormant in all the arts, and enthusiasm was almost a vice, William Blake (1757-1827) was destined to be the forerunner of the Romantic Movement both in art and poetry. His sustenance, such as it was, came from his engravings, but his fame to posterity lies in his art, and in the remarkable books of prose, poetry and prophecy which he wrote, illustrated, engraved, and printed himself. This unusual method of publishing his volumes originated not from want of a publisher, but because of artistic choice, and because he wished to indulge all his gifts at the same time.

Blake's method, as can be seen only by visits to museum libraries, produced volumes of surpassing beauty, and it may be of interest to read Mr. John Sampson's faithful description of the method itself: "The text and the surrounding design were written in reverse (a painfully laborious method), in a medium impervious to acid upon small copper plates about 5 x 3 inches, which were then etched in a bath of aqua-fortis until the work stood in relief as in a stereotype. From these plates, which to economize copper were, in many cases, engraved upon both sides, impressions were printed, in the ordinary manner, in tints made to harmonize with the colour scheme afterwards applied by the artist."

A generation or so ahead of most of the Romanticists, Blake was appreciated by only a few of his contemporaries, notably Charles Lamb, who looked upon him as "one of the most extraordinary persons of the age." A hundred years after his death, the reaction to his long depreciation became so pronounced as to almost turn reasonable appreciation into uncritical adulation. One of the finest and soundest criticisms of William Blake was written by Arthur Symons, who said: "Had it not been for his lack of a technical knowledge of music, had he been able to write down his inventions in that art also, he would have left us the creation of something like an universal art. That universal art he did, during his lifetime, create; for he sang his songs to his own music; and thus, while he lived, he was the complete realization of the poet in all his faculties, and the only complete realization that has ever been known."

Blake should have been his own illustrator for *The Tiger* but, failing that, we quote Blake as justification for choosing Theodore Ross. Blake said: "Shall painting be confined to the sordid drudgery of facsimile reproductions . . . and not be, as poetry and music are, elevated into its own proper sphere of invention and visionary perception?" And Ross, though his expert knowledge of animal anatomy placed him on the staff of the Rockefeller Institute, does not allow knowledge to restrict his imagination in the portrayal of animals on canvas.

[11]

Ross is also comparable to Blake in that he does many things well. He is a graduate chemist, an archeologist (he was a member of Count Prorok's expedition to Carthage to dig Roman and Punic graves), a zoologist, printer, and champion chess player.

Carl J. H. Anderson started way back in the time of McKinley by sweeping floors, making fires and cleaning spittoons (we have his own word for that). The next milestone in his career found him setting type for a country newspaper in South Dakota, running the paper off on a Washington Hand Press, collecting news items and overdue bills, and heckling jobbers. Back of it all glowed an ambition—to become a master printer—which led him through many arduous years and culminated in the appearance of his splendid edition of *Treasure Island*. He made his *Treasure Island* "not for boys," he says, "I made it for men, but only for those who have retained the enthusiasm of youth. Had Justis illustrate it with tough mugs with hair on their hairy chests. Put fine rag paper into it; printed it beautifully; bound it in an imported linen canvas; stamped it in blood red and cased it in a slip cover as black as the black hearts of Morgan, Pew, Black Dog, and the rest of that murderous crew." And, we might add, thereby won himself a place in the American Institute of Graphic Arts 1931 Exhibition of Fifty Books of the Year.

Mr. Anderson's plan was to produce fine editions—equal to those selling from $25 to $75 in limited editions—at a price the average man could afford to pay, by selling them on a subscription plan at $6.50 each for a group of six. After *Treasure Island* the business depression temporarily shelved the project, but Mr. Anderson hopes—and we hope—that the plan may be carried out as conditions improve.

In his edition of *The Tiger*, Mr. Anderson used Mercure, Nicholas Cochin Bold and Nicholas Cochin Italic for the title page, Mercure and Nicholas Cochin Bold for the text. The illustration was reproduced with water color inks—three colors and black—and gold metallic ink. The gold was printed with one impression. The three blues were printed from rubber, the black and gold from zinc plates. The all-over tint on the title page was printed with water color ink from a solid rubber plate.

Much of the force of *The Tiger* lies in its strong contrasts of white, black, and bright colors. Here the paper was of value not only as a background for the printing, but also to provide the contrast Mr. Anderson wanted. He wisely chose Linweave Text for its dazzling whiteness and for its antique finish, which is particularly well adapted to water color printing.

KUBLA KHAN

by SAMUEL TAYLOR COLERIDGE, *illustrated by* URIEL
printed by the ROGERS-KELLOGG-STILLSON COMPANY
on Linweave Oxford, White, Vellum Finish and Linweave Milano, Peachbeige

A CONTEMPORARY of Leigh Hunt and Robert Southey, both of whose work is represented in the Linweave Limited Editions for 1931, Samuel Taylor Coleridge was easily the most inspired poet of the three, being, with Wordsworth, the leader of the renaissance of poetry which swept England early in the nineteenth century. Nearly all anthologies of English poetry carry one or more of his three best-known works, *The Rime of the Ancient Mariner*, *Christabel*, and *Kubla Khan*. In middle age Coleridge suffered two failings which brought upon him the malediction of the crowd: a weak will, and an affinity for the refuge of opium. It was during the repose which follows recourse to the drug that *Kubla Khan* came to him as a dream— literally hundreds of lines of verse, composed, rhymed, scanned, polished—without a conscious thought to help give them being. Awakening, he scribbled them on paper as rapidly as his pen would write. Before he could finish a visitor came, and when he returned to the task the remainder of the dream escaped his memory.

To reproduce a vision so bizarre and fanciful and beautiful seemed almost beyond hope until Alexander King, with happy inspiration, suggested Uriel Birnbaum. Uriel (as he signs his paintings) is an Austrian who dwells in Vienna and travels extensively in Palestine, where he has already visited all the sacred places of the Bible. He stands foremost among mid-European artists, and many critics agree that for beauty of color and dramatic strength his illustrations for books are at present unsurpassed. His work is unusually grotesque and bizarre, always sincere, and is marked by a richness of fancy which has made his Biblical subjects, above all, world renowned. He is deeply religious—believed in the war as a visitation of God in judgment of mankind, offered himself up in active service, was severely wounded and lost a foot. To him the five books of Moses are the Word of God, and he has illustrated them with rare insight, power and sincerity.

Like Blake, Uriel is artist, poet and writer. As a respite, perhaps, from his more rigorous work he has written and illustrated several charming children's books now being published in Austria. The finest example of his astonishing versatility is an autobiographical book of sonnets, *In God's War*, written during the war, and since illustrated by his own pen and ink drawings, which depict his wartime temptations, his being wounded and cared for in hospitals, his recall from the very door of death, and his courtship of the nurse who later became his wife. It is unfortunate that the book has not yet been published in English, for one European critic has rabidly termed it the one book about the war which must be read.

Rogers and Kellogg and Stillson were three old established printers with young ideas who merged into one tremendous unit the better to take advantage of the rapid strides being made in printing processes. Two years after the merger the Rogers-Kellogg-Stillson Company had installed and were operating complete equipment for offset, water color, letterpress and Intensatone printing. They believe that the new processes, individually and in combination, offer greater flexibility and fidelity in the reproduction of tricky and difficult illustrations; that they make possible substantial economies which benefit both the printer and the buyer of printing; and that the trend of printing in the next few years will be toward experimentation with the new processes, new type faces, and striking new papers, rather than rigid adherence to established printing principles.

Entrusted with *Kubla Khan*, they set about to demonstrate. The titles, imbued with the oriental flavor of the poem, are set in Civilité, a revival of the face originally designed by Robert Granjon of Paris in the middle sixteenth century. The text is set in Kabel Bold whose long ascenders and bold simplicity blend well with Uriel's painting. "The text and title page," they thought, "demand a soft paper; the illustration, one with a harder surface. Why compromise on only one paper? Why not use a tip-in and get maximum effect throughout?"

So the text appears on Linweave Milano, Peachbeige, one of the four lovely colors available in the same mellow sheet on which *The Course* is printed. The illustration is on Linweave Oxford, a moderately priced vellum which adapts itself as admirably to offset work as does Milano to line, water color, and Ben Day work. To capture the depth and glow of Uriel's colors, seven offset colors were used for the tip-in, while the title page required four colors and was printed by letterpress and Ben Day. The result you can judge for yourself.

The Rogers-Kellogg-Stillson Company likes to be known as an organization rather than as a collection of individuals. However, if any personal credit is due for this edition of *Kubla Khan*, it must go to Ralph M. Duenewald, an energetic young Chicagoan who for ten years superintended the Mount Vernon plant of William Edwin Rudge and who now devotes his talent to the production of fine printing for the new combine.

AFTER BLENHEIM

by ROBERT SOUTHEY, *illustrated with a photograph by* PAUL HESSE
designed and printed by NORMAN T. A. MUNDER & CO.
on Linweave Japan, Ivory, Plate Finish

To THE host of stories you know about students expelled from college who later became leaders in thought and industry, add that back in the late eighteenth century Westminster expelled a young man named Robert Southey for writing a sarcastic essay on flogging, and that years later England turned around and made him poet-laureate. Yet Robert Southey was not a major poet. Of the three Lake Poets (so called because of their long residence in England's Lake Country) Coleridge and Wordsworth were easily the better poets, but Southey was by far the most versatile writer, devoting a long and unselfish lifetime to production of verse, prose, history, biography, and political essays of unfailingly high caliber.

Never a rich man, nor even a well-to-do man, Southey was a faithful and generous husband, friend and father. It so happened that he and Coleridge and Robert Lovell married three sisters. After Lovell's death and the wayward departure of Coleridge, Southey without hesitancy took into his own home his two sisters-in-law and their children, ungrudgingly working the harder to provide shelter and sustenance. A fine tribute to a loyal and kindly man are Walter Savage Landor's lines to Southey:

"No firmer breast than thine hath Heaven
To poet, sage or hero given:
No heart more tender, none more just,
To that he largely placed in trust:
Therefore shalt thou, whatever date
Of years be thine, with soul elate
Rise up before the eternal throne,
And hear, in God's own voice, 'Well done!'"

[14]

After Blenheim, sometimes known as *The Battle of Blenheim*, was written in Southey's twenty-fourth year and shows promise of the vigor of mind and store of knowledge which eventually made him, in the words of Lord Byron, "the only existing entire man of letters." The battle of Blenheim was one of the encounters in the war of the Spanish succession. It occurred August 13, 1704, near the village of Bavaria on the left bank of the Danube in Southwestern Germany. The French and Bavarians under Marshals Tallard and Marsin were put to rout by the English and Austrians under the Duke of Marlborough and Prince Eugene. The irony of Southey's lines, however, seems as applicable to the late great War as it did to Blenheim two hundred years ago!

So rapidly has photography progressed in the past decade that no series of this sort would be quite complete without at least one example. *After Blenheim* being the one selection best suited to photographic treatment, Paul Hesse automatically became the one logical photographer to handle the assignment. His keen sense of dramatic composition and his nice flair for correct detail were clearly indicated by the nature of the subject. Packing a pair of geese, an equal number of children, one grand old man, his capable brother Otto, and untold paraphernalia into a convenient truck, he set out for location. It was a tough assignment but he handled it with customary finesse.

Paul Hesse was born in Brooklyn not so many years ago. His first love was a small and battered Brownie camera, from which attachment he was for many years dissuaded by sundry relatives, governments, and circumstances which caused him in turn to become medical student, actor, soldier, and artist. It was during his sojourn in France that the bully of the outfit, nearly twice his size, so goaded him on the neatness of his person and appearance that Hesse finally took him behind a barn and gave him a sound thrashing, to the open delight of the whole regiment. After the war he painted covers for Collier's and made an occasional portrait photograph, notably one of Lady Diana Manners as the Nun in *The Miracle*.

At long last his camera reclaimed him and he quickly gained for himself a place well forward in the select list of artist-photographers. Today, when he is not busy making photographs, he lives in Silvermine, Connecticut, in a charming colonial house which he had transplanted rafter for rafter from Stepney—twenty miles away. He hunts and fishes on every possible occasion, and is raising an enviable collection of ducks, chickens and children.

To many printers the reproduction of a halftone on laid paper holds more terrors than even the successful posing of two impatient children and a pair of recalcitrant geese! But not to Norman T. A. Munder, whose consistently fine reproduction of halftones on any and all kinds of paper is a constant reproof to those printers who sacrifice the effectiveness of halftones on beautiful paper to pursue the somewhat easier course of perpetually reverting to coated papers of far less charm and beauty.

For many years now Mr. Munder has been busy at his shop in Baltimore, producing printing of as uniformly high quality as you are likely to find anywhere in America. His work possesses a gentle charm and old-world dignity which affords pleasant and often welcome contrast to more raucous modern productions. His consummate passion for getting every detail exactly right has built around him a tradition of fine craftsmanship which in turn has made him one of America's most highly respected and best loved printers.

For the typography of *After Blenheim*, Mr. Munder used French Old Style and Goudy Text. His paper selection was Linweave Text, Ivory, in the plate finish which is prepared expressly for reproduction of halftones. In brochures and books containing much text and occasional halftones, Mr. Munder has recently achieved splendid results by the use of Linweave Text, Antique Finish for the text, and Linweave Text, Plate Finish for the halftones. His choice of the Ivory shade for *After Blenheim* was appropriate, and makes an excellent showing of one of the seven interesting colors in which Linweave Text is manufactured.

ABOU BEN ADHEM

by LEIGH HUNT, *illustrated by* JACK PERKINS
designed by CATHARINE MELLEN, *printed by* THE ALDUS PRINTERS
on Linweave Japan, White, Antique

STILL a third popular figure in the Romantic Movement in English literature is represented in the Linweave Limited Editions with the inclusion of *Abou Ben Adhem*. On the headstone of James Henry Leigh Hunt, 1784-1859, might well have been written, "Poet, essayist, critic, editor, publisher, patriot." Instead, his monument in Kensal Green Cemetery, London, carries the simple inscription, "Write me as one that loves his fellow men." Which is as it should be, for Leigh Hunt was above all a humanist, and in no other work did he so clearly reveal the inviolable idealism which guided his life as in *Abou Ben Adhem*, the poem which brought him greatest popular renown and which he himself numbered among the five or six of his works he liked best.

Into the capable hands of two comparatively young artists was given the pleasant task of designing the edition. Jack Perkins of Boston (many the children who have reveled in his fairy-tale extravaganzas) painted the illustration—an unusual combination of oil and water color, antiqued to produce a soft, rich lustre. Catharine Mellen delved into the New York Public Library's bag of antiquities and emerged with decorations which blend with the illustration as charmingly as they conform to the decorative feeling of the time and locale of the poem.

Aside from illustrating children's books, Jack Perkins designs book jackets and indulges his hobby for painting and antiquing screens, which are every bit as striking as his illustration for *Abou Ben Adhem*. He wants some day to illustrate limited editions; his big ambition is to do *Faust*. Catharine Mellen graduated from Parsons Art School just four years ago, and went right to work for Aldus, where she has since been responsible for much of the artistry for which Aldus productions are noted.

Ten years ago, George Messing, Frank Henahan and Bert Chambers were three men with ideals and very little money. But they wangled a small plant, chose the ambitious name Aldus (after the famous fifteenth century Italian printer who, among other things, invented italics), hitched their wagon to a star, and applied the whip. Theirs is an extremely modern viewpoint: they are constantly alert for any new idea, process, or type face, which will add legitimate beauty to their printing, and which will keep their productions a leap or two ahead of the common run. They were responsible for the invention and introduction of water color printing into this country and hold the Jean Berté patents covering the process. Their rise in the printing world has been quite phenomenal and they gained additional fame a year or two ago when they were entrusted with the limited editions of Lynd Ward's now famous novels in woodcuts. Through a recent merger with the Bartlett-Orr Press, The Aldus Printers are now an integral part of the Bartlett-Aldus Press where increased facilities should enable them to do even more startling things in their chosen field of modern printing. One of their first assignments under the new banner is a limited edition of *Faust* for The Limited Editions Club, Inc., which, under the able direction of George Macy, is producing some of the finest books in America.

For the difficult reproduction of the Perkins painting, five offset colors and one letterpress color were used, while a sixth offset impression produced the grey tint beneath the type and decoration. The type selection is Civilité, the face used for the titles of *Kubla Kahn*, and probably the nearest approach to Persian calligraphy ever pied by an over-zealous typographer. The paper is the same soft-textured Linweave Japan on which *The Lute Girl* was printed, except that the color is white instead of the ivory used for the earlier edition.

TO HELEN

by Edgar Allan Poe, *illustrated by* Carolyn Edmundson
printed by Carl Purington Rollins *at the Printing-Office of the Yale University Press on Linweave Japan, White, Halftone Finish*

AMID the poverty, intemperance, ill health, and brave useless hope of his later years, Edgar Allan Poe's courtship of Sarah Helen Whitman stands as a gleaming interlude in the life of the poet. Both were advanced in years, both were poets, death had put an untimely end to each of their early ventures in marriage, their birthdays fell on the same date—all in all they seemed fated for each other. Perhaps, as some biographers maintain, Poe's love for the fascinating widow was of the mind rather than of the heart. Perhaps his motives *were* monetary rather than deeply amorous. Nevertheless, the famous courtship produced the most inspired correspondence and one of the most impassioned poems in the English language, a poem written when America's greatest and most unfortunate man of letters was tottering on the brink of incipient insanity. Shortly after its appearance, Poe in 1849 on the last trip he was ever to make, wrote his devoted mother-in-law a brief letter from Richmond, the last paragraph of which sums up the pathos and terrible futility of his last year on earth:

"... I got here with two dollars over—of which I enclose you one. Oh, God, my Mother, shall we ever meet again? If possible, Oh, COME! My clothes are so horrible and I am so ill. Oh, if you could come to me, my mother. Write instantly—Oh do not fail. God forever bless you."

To Helen was the second poem of the same name composed by Poe, for whom the name Helen seemed to hold a curious spiritual association. The first, written in his youth to the mother of a boyhood friend, contains the immortal lines, "...To the glory that was Greece and the grandeur that was Rome," and is more widely known but surely no more likely to endure than the lines reproduced herein.

A glimpse one evening of Mrs. Whitman on her doorstep in Providence inspired Poe to "dream a dream" of "Helen." The resultant poem crystallizes the dream rather than the actual setting in which he found her, and it is this interpretation which Carolyn Edmundson has followed in painting the glorious illustration which adorns this edition. Though but recently arrived at voting age, Miss Edmundson has already won a prominent niche among American illustrators with her splendid work for *Vogue, Harper's Bazaar, Woman's Home Companion,* and *Delineator.* At present she is engaged in painting portraits of prominent men, and hopes soon to illustrate fine editions.

It is a far cry to the day when Carl Purington Rollins, aged 11, began fussing about the pressroom of the old *Messenger* in West Newbury, Massachusetts. But from then on through the fruitful years of his own Montague Press up to his present position as Printer to Yale University, his climb to the top of the printing profession has been inevitable. It was at Rollins' Montague Press, located in the old Dyke Mill at Montague, Massachusetts, that Bruce Rogers first used Centaur type in the eight-page booklet *Centaur* which is now so avidly sought by collectors. Rollins still owns the Dyke Mill and returns there every summer with his family. He and his wife, Margaret Rollins, also have a hand press at their home in New Haven on which they print charming volumes with the imprint of their own private press, *At the Sign of the Chorobates.* Because he so consistently raises printing and bookmaking to the level of artistic achievement, Mr. Rollins is the recipient from Yale University of an honorary degree of Master of Arts.

For his edition of *To Helen,* Mr. Rollins chose to use Linotype Baskerville and Bulmer Italic, transitional type faces of the late eighteenth and early nineteenth centuries. The illustration has been done in four-color process—white, red, blue, and black. The paper, believe it or not, is identically the same sheet as was used for *Abou Ben Adhem,* which immediately precedes *To Helen* in this volume. There is, however, one major exception: the Linweave Japan used for *Abou Ben Adhem* has a soft, antique finish; the Linweave Japan used for *To Helen* has a harder, plated finish for the reproduction of halftones. The result is a paper with a finish of real distinction and beauty which will still take halftones and process plates successfully—a combination hitherto difficult if not downright impossible to achieve.

NON SUM QUALIS ERAM BONAE SUB REGNO CYNARAE

by ERNEST DOWSON, *illustrated by* JEFFERSON CLARK
designed and printed by FRED ANTHOENSEN *at the Southworth Press*
on Linweave Text, White, Wove

THE close of the nineteenth century saw a quickening of life in English art, literature, and manners, as though people tired of the artistic and intellectual monotony of the preceding decades, and with fresh curiosity sought new sensations, new expression. As a result the eighteen nineties became a distinctive epoch in art and ideas; an epoch of experiment, achievement, and a few regrets; an epoch which despite its stigma of decadence seems in retrospect to have been the spark which set off the twentieth century's rapid advancement—in living, if not in art and literature. The desire to include in the Linweave Limited Editions some representative selection of the period led ultimately to the choice of *Non Sum Qualis Eram Bonae Sub Regno Cynarae*, an exquisite poem symbolic of the decadence in which Ernest Dowson linked an eternal and bitter anguish of the soul with modern emotion.

Dowson was a young man, fragile in body and sensitive in spirit, when he wrote the slim volume of verse which composes his entire literary output. In an age which boasted such names as Swinburne, Thompson, Meredith, Wilde, and Beerbohm, Dowson was looked upon by his contemporaries as one of the minor poets of the time. Yet in the brief score and a half years since his death, his poetry has achieved almost classical rank.

Dowson was still a young man when he died, his body racked by disease, his spirit broken by the calamitous love affair which he has immortalized in verse. The object of his consuming love was a French girl whose mother kept a small restaurant in Soho—a pleasant, matter-of-fact girl with no deep affection for Dowson. After two years courtship, during which Dowson allowed an illusion of reciprocal love on her part to blind him completely, she married a waiter and dealt Dowson a blow from which he never recovered. Dowson's only epigram tells the whole story:

"Because I am idolatrous and have besought,
  With grievous supplication and consuming prayer,
  The admirable image that my dreams have wrought
  Out of her swan's neck and her dark abundant hair:
  The jealous gods, who brook no worship save their own,
  Turned my live idol and her heart to stone."

Somewhat reminiscent of the black and white work of Aubrey Beardsley, another bright star of the eighteen nineties, but infinitely finer in detail is the delicate pen and ink drawing by Jefferson Clark which illustrates this edition of *Cynara*. Born in New York of a family of artists, Jefferson Clark studied with Carriere in Paris and Stuck in Munich, and has exhibited in practically every European gallery. Only once before has his work been reproduced. In 1923 the Thyrsos Verlag in Vienna published a seven-page pamphlet of his work, which is today one of the most eagerly sought publishing rarities, one copy recently selling for $250 at Drouot's auction in Paris. Like John Burlin's drawing for *The Course*, Clark's illustration for *Cynara* is the first he has ever made expressly for reproduction.

Fred Anthoensen has literally grown up with The Southworth Press, starting many years ago as compositor and progressing steadily to his present position as manager of a press notable for its type equipment and for the hundred or more books he has designed and printed. Books are his hobby, both as a printer and a collector. His own work shows the masterly restraint of the true scholar of printing and he possesses an uncanny ability to interpret correctly in type and design the content of the book he is printing.

In the production of *Cynara*, Mr. Anthoensen exceeded the fondest expectations of everyone concerned with the venture. The extremely difficult linecut (and what a ticklish job of plate-making that was!) is magnificently printed; his type and ornament selections reveal true artistry and perfect taste. Caslon 471 is used for the title page in conjunction with Bell Italics, which also appear in the text. The Bell type was designed in London by John Bell, famous proprietor of Bell's British Theatre, Bell's *Poets of Great Britain*, and Bell's *Shakespeare*. The punches were cut by Richard Austin, and the type was first cast by Bell's British Letter Foundry in 1788. The original matrices are now owned by Stephenson, Blake & Co., Ltd. of Sheffield, England where several sizes were cast and sent to America especially for use in the Linweave edition of *Cynara*. The decorative material on the title page was imported from the same firm. In 1864 Henry Oscar Houghton imported some of the Bell type for his Riverside Press at Cambridge, Massachusetts. Bruce Rogers liked it, and used it in some of the Riverside Press Limited Editions, but not knowing its origin he called it Brimmer. Stanley Morison discovered its true source in 1930 and it will henceforth be known as Bell.

The Tiger presents Linweave Text with an Antique Finish. *After Blenheim* shows the adaptability of Linweave Text with a Plate Finish. In *Cynara*, this paper of seemingly endless possibilities is presented in still a third guise—this time as a *wove* paper without the laid marks which are present in the other two editions. If you wonder where Linweave Text, Wove, fits into the picture, examine carefully the fine, intricate lines of Jefferson Clark's drawing and see if you can find one place where the ink has filled in! Linweave Text, Wove, like Linweave Text, Laid, is made in Plate as well as Antique Finish, and all four are stock papers.

THE CONGO
by VACHEL LINDSAY, *illustrated by* ALEXANDER KING
designed and printed by THE PRINTING HOUSE OF WILLIAM EDWIN RUDGE
on Linweave Text, Sun Tan, Antique

DURING the summer of 1912 an unknown poet and apostle trudged happily from Illinois to New Mexico, preaching the Gospel of Beauty, trading rhymes of his own making for food and shelter warmly given. Returning, he settled in his own home town of Springfield, Illinois, and became a local booster—not for bigger trade and better industry, but for greater beauty and a higher plane of living. Forceful poems appeared, rich in the color and idiom of the local townsfolk, couched in the rhythm of revivalist chants, preaching the beauty and salvation awaiting all mankind, whatever its plight. And so the message of Vachel Lindsay was given the world—in the magnificent poems of which *The Congo* is most widely known.

Nicholas Vachel Lindsay was born in Springfield, Illinois, November 10, 1879, in the same house in which he now abides. After an extensive education he at once became a lecturer and in 1906 began the first of the long walking tours which culminated in the pilgrimage of 1912. In 1909 and 1910 he temporarily dropped his "gospel of beauty" to lecture for the Anti-Saloon League throughout Central Illinois.

"Lindsay," writes Louis Untermeyer, "created his poetry to reach the public—all of his verse being written in his role of apostle. He was, primarily, a rhyming John the Baptist singing to convert the heathen, to stimulate and encourage the half-hearted dreams that hide and are lost in our sordid villages and townships . . . In *The Congo and Other Poems* (1914), an infectious blend of rhyme, religion and ragtime . . . he struck his most powerful—and most popular—vein."

Given *The Congo* to illustrate, Alexander King promptly entered seventh heaven. Having haunted Harlem many nights and roamed the Congo many months he knew to a nicety the people of the poem; he had laughed with the "fat black bucks" and talked with the "skull-faced witch-men lean," and he owned the artistic skill to portray with faithful detail and happy imagination the characters Lindsay had seen and envisioned. Paintings for *The Congo* were quickly added to the long list of distinguished illustrations Mr. King has made for American book publishers—illustrations for *Tom Jones, Salammbo, The Magic Island, Gulliver's Travels,* the plays of Eugene O'Neill and some dozen others.

At 31, Alexander King is an accomplished artist, a brilliant conversationalist, and a keen critic of world literature. His collection of fine editions and periodicals is one which any collector might well envy. Born in Vienna, he studied there at the Secession School of Art at whose head was Gustav Klimt, the instigator in 1903 of the modern revolution in design, and a designer of what we now call "modern furniture" long before the advent of the American architecture upon which the design of modern furniture is commonly supposed to be based.

In the brief years since he bid *adieu* to school, Alexander King has traveled widely and with open eyes, including in his itinerary a long stay in Tunisia, and nine months in the French Congo. A few years ago he exhibited at the Granoff galleries in Paris in conjunction with George Grosz and Franz Masereel, two of Europe's foremost artists. He was later tendered a one-man show at the Gallerie Billiet in Paris. A complete bibliography of his work will shortly be published under the imprint of The Brown House, probably the first time in history that an artist has had a published bibliography!

The Congo was one of the last productions of William Edwin Rudge, whose untimely death last summer robbed the world of a master printer, an artist, a loyal friend of young men with ideas, a discerning publisher, and a fine, kindly gentleman. During his forty-three years in the printing and publishing business, his fine books and fine printing gained such international prominence that Herbert Hoover, then Secretary of Commerce, appointed him to represent American printing at the International Exposition of Modern Decorative and Industrial Art at Paris in 1925. To the world of art and printing his death is a severe loss but his accomplishments will live as a standard to follow for many years to come.

For the typography of *The Congo*, Mr. Rudge selected the Metro Series, recently designed by W. A. Dwiggins to show in part the unexplored possibilities of design in the so-called Gothics. It is an entirely original series of sans-serif faces whose bold black lines seem aptly suited for *The Congo*.

In *The Tiger*, water color is beautifully printed on Linweave Text. In *After Blenheim* a photograph is reproduced on Linweave Text through the medium of a halftone, with telling effect. In *Cynara*, Linweave Text demonstrated how well a really good paper should take a delicate linecut. Now, in *The Congo*, we find this astonishing paper serving as a medium for offset printing—and doing very well, thank you! The illustrations are printed in two and three colors on another of the seven very useful shades in which Linweave Text is made.

A BIRD IN A GILDED CAGE

by ARTHUR LAMB and HARRY VON TILZER
illustrated by JOHN HELD, JR., printed by HAL MARCHBANKS at the Marchbanks Press
on Linweave Romney, Ivory

FOR weeks it was a moot question whether or not a series so sincere in purpose as the Linweave Limited Editions should include a selection in lighter vein. But what good is stew without salt, or coffee without cream, or bread without leaven? It was finally agreed that a bit of spice might well be relished by the recipients of the series.

So, to every lover of close harmony, to all of you whose eyes take on a reminiscent sparkle at mention of the mellow nineties, and particularly to Harry Von Tilzer whose facile pen immortalized the sentimental ballad, the Linweave Limited Edition of *A Bird in a Gilded Cage* is affectionately dedicated.

Harry Von Tilzer has written thousands of songs, a dozen or so of which have sold more than a million copies, but he still keeps on working. You can find him most any day in his little office on Broadway—dapper, good-natured, showing his years neither in spirit nor appearance, always willing to talk a bit about the old days when song writing was a pleasant and lucrative task. *A Bird in a Gilded Cage* was "the key that opened the door of wealth and fame" for him. Arthur Lamb, an Englishman who died only two years ago, wrote the words in 1899 and brought them to Mr. Von Tilzer one day in Chicago. That night, in a roadhouse of questionable repute, he composed the tune whose echoes still may be heard on very clear nights. Mr. Von Tilzer has been responsible for scores of hits, including such classics as *Down Where the Wurzburger Flows, The Cubanola Glide, Alexander, I Want a Girl, Down on the Farm,* and *On the Old Fall River Line.*

John Held, Jr. made the illustrations for *A Bird in a Gilded Cage*—that old sentimentalist who engraved his first commercial woodcut at the age of 11, and whose incomparable engravings of the mauve decade adorn such fine editions as *The Saga of Frankie and Johnny* and *Baron Munchausen*—the latter printed by Hal Marchbanks, who also printed this present edition. Three other of the recent editions he has illustrated have a decidedly anti-Prohibition tinge—*My Pious Friends and Drunken Companions, Drawn from the Wood,* and *The Saloon in the Home.* Concurrently, many and varied of his engravings may be seen in *The New Yorker* and in *Liberty,* where he has also revived the modern flapper he made famous a few years ago.

About the time Hal Marchbanks got old enough to be of some help around his father's cattle ranch in Ennis, Texas, the local printer advertised for an apprentice. Young Marchbanks applied for the job and got it, being the only applicant. After he had collected a vast store of amusing stories about the itinerant printers of the early days, ambition spurred him north to establish Hal Marchbanks' Print Shop on the Tow Path at Lockport, N.Y., where he served notice of his intentions in an announcement which contained one bit of solicitation well worth repeating: "Our telephone is Bell 3964 and upon invitation we will come to your office, thus saving you the trouble of looking up a printer." Despite the announcement, business was scarce and Hal Marchbanks finally moved to New York City where, at the present time, the Marchbanks Press is adding materially to America's yearly crop of really fine printing.

With the publication of *A Bird in a Gilded Cage,* Linweave Romney made its first public appearance. It is a beautifully soft paper with both laid and felt marks, in white and four unusual colors. One of its unique features is that the standard size sheet cuts without waste to five announcement sizes, which fit envelopes to match and allow boundless opportunity for economy in the print shop.

EVERY bit as interesting as the story of the ten editions is the story of the making of the bound book you now hold in your hands. Every bit as valuable as the editions, too, are the preliminary pages and introduction, designed by Frederic Goudy, and printed at Utica, N.Y. by Howard Coggeshall and Willett Sherwood of Coggeshall-Sherwood, Inc.

The type faces designed by Frederic W. Goudy flow in a golden stream across more fine book pages, more pages in the advertising and periodical literature of the world, than the type faces of any other master, living or dead. Since January 1, 1926 he has designed twenty-six new types. In two decades he has attained a total of seventy different designs. The greater number of these are in everyday use wherever the Roman alphabet is known—many of them will continue to beautify the finest pages from the finest presses as long as our civilization lasts. Kennerley, Forum Title, Garamont, Goudy Modern, Goudy Newstyle, Goudy Oldstyle, Italian Oldstyle, Deepdene, Marlboro, Goudy Text and Lombardic Capitals, Trajan, Hadriano, Truesdell, Mediaeval, Kaatskill—no end of them.

He makes his drawings, cuts the card patterns, tools the smaller metal patterns. He engraves the matrices with tools made with his own hands, and then casts the first types made from these matrices. To our knowledge no other designer has ever perfected his art to a point where he performed all of these operations himself. He works with the sureness born of a scholarly understanding of types, their readability, and their adaptability to the highest demands the art preservative can impose. He hopes to live to bequeath a hundred type faces to posterity.

Mr. Goudy does not believe genius has very much to do with type designing. High ideals, hard work, long hours, tireless research—these are the ingredients he skillfully blends into every type face he makes. When he is at Deepdene, the Goudy home at Marlboro-on-Hudson, he is certain to be found either at his drawing board in the library, or over in the old mill by the brook, where he has his workshop. Offer him that which he most desires in life, and he will ask only that he be left alone to do his work.

Perhaps he takes an evening off—spends it reminiscing with friends whom he and Mrs. Goudy are entertaining over the week-end. The lights are off at 11 o'clock and all retire. All except Goudy, who says "Good night," steals softly down the stairs, and into the library. He is at his drawing board again until after 1, when he feels sleepy, goes to bed. A guest, who thinks he is first up in the morning, appears in the library at 8 o'clock. Goudy is there, bent over his drawing board. He has been there since 6. And the final drawing for his popular Deepdene Italic is finished before he sits down to breakfast! A doctor advises him to reduce his daily working hours to four. He compromises by cutting from sixteen to twelve.

Old enough to have become, like Leonardo da Vinci, a legend in his own time, he is still young enough to drive his Cadillac five hundred miles in a single day, as he did on the last lap of his journey home from the Pacific Coast in October of this year. He returned just in time to design the introduction for this book, choosing Deepdene and Deepdene Italic for the body, Trajan for the title page and cover, and Deepdene Open Text for the headings. The 36-point Trajan on the title page was expressly cut for this edition. The initial at the beginning of this article is also from Goudy's versatile hand.

To his good friend, Howard W. Coggeshall, goes the credit for persuading Mr. Goudy to take an active hand in the preparation of this book. Entrusted with the assignment, Mr. Coggeshall, himself a designer of excellent taste and wide renown, unhesitatingly recommended that his more famous fellow-craftsman design the part of the work he was to print.

If it ever occurs to you to wonder why a craftsman of Mr. Coggeshall's rank is content to remain in Utica while all his contemporaries flock to the larger and supposedly more lucrative centers, bear in mind that central New York State is Mr. Coggeshall's home and almost always has been, and that people reared in that benign atmosphere of lakes and foothills are quite reasonably likely to be homesick away from it for any length of time. We personally are glad Mr. Coggeshall chooses to remain where he is, solely because there he furnishes glowing proof of one of our own long-cherished theories—that genius flowers every bit as fruitfully on native soil as it does transplanted to those cramped and crowded centers where youths of promise are shipped to win their fame and fortune.

Born in Morris, N.Y., Howard Coggeshall first smelled printers' ink in a typical country newspaper office of the eighteen nineties, where he worked ten hours a day—and most of Tuesday night—for the extravagant sum of $2.50 a week (and that is *not* a misprint). He didn't mind the wages particularly, nor the 10-hour day (for after all, he was learning a trade). But when after two years he did enter a formal complaint regarding the 35-hour Tuesday-Wednesday shift, his indignant employer promptly fired him, thereby doing him the greatest kindness of his life. After a considerable interval of newspaper reporting, Mr. Coggeshall inevitably returned to printing, eventually establishing the present plant of Coggeshall-Sherwood, Inc. in association with his capable friend and partner, Willett B. Sherwood.

The preliminary matter and introduction are printed on Linweave Text—you probably remember hearing that name before!—White Wove, the same paper on which Mr. Anthoensen printed *Cynara*, and as excellent a selection for the purpose as you are likely to find, even among much higher priced papers.

With all the ingredients of a book at hand, it next became necessary to find someone to apply the finishing touch. By the very nature of their make-up, the Linweave Limited Editions are more or less personal messages from the craftsmen responsible for their being. In putting them together in permanent form, we naturally sought a bookbinder who could infuse personality into the binding as did the printers into the composition and presswork. There seemed but one logical choice, and so the task was given over to Raymond E. Baylis and Randall W. Bergmann of the Eugene C. Lewis Company in New York, a bindery with a background of 39 years' distinguished service to the printers and publishers of America.

Just as good printing requires more than paper and type alone, good bookbinding demands more than mere material and workmanship. Because Mr. Baylis and Mr. Bergmann and their associates have given this book the rare touch of personality that marks the difference between an ordinary job and a book of distinction, we believe you will agree that theirs is a worthwhile contribution to the illustrious craftsmanship assembled under the Linweave banner.

In passing on, let us say that it has been a fascinating task to study the lives and works of the authors who appear in these pages, to meet and work with and know the artists and printers who have contributed so notably to the editions which follow. If you enjoy reading and studying and gloating over the editions one-tenth as much as we enjoyed preparing them we shall be very happy.

But, pleasant or not, it has been a colossal task, and as we pen these last few lines, we cannot help muttering to ourselves the sympathetic philosophy of Harry Von Tilzer, "she is happier here at rest."

W. L.
Springfield, Mass., Nov. 10, 1931

THE COURSE

By Daniel Chase

An Introduction to his novel "The Middle Passage"

Reprinted by permission of The Macmillan Company, publishers

Illustrated by John Burlin; printed by D. B. Updike

The Merrymount Press, Boston

The paper is Linweave Milano, White Jade

Linweave Limited Editions

1931

The Course

FOR you have first the long run eastward under the trades to the Guinea coast, a pale belt of melted jade under an African moon thin-edged and figured like a worn doubloon. And then, your black cargo ironed between decks, there comes the Middle Passage, to Cuba or to Brazil; a hell of uncertainty, of blind haste, of suffering, and of death in strange forms. And at last, cargo delivered, you laze northward into cleaner seas, home ports. . . . And these three passages are like life itself. For you have your youth, and you raise your coasts of romance, faint and fragrant clouds under the silver ghost of a waning moon. And you have, too, your long run home, with steady winds, a sure port at the end. But between — a time of uncertainty, of suffering; you come through or you don't; you're broken or made in the Middle Passage, this feverish interlude between the outward passage of youth and the homeward passage of age. . . . But all of life is really a Middle Passage, a dark flight through unknown seas between two shores, both dim, half-guessed, ill-charted. But at the end is freedom, not slavery; death, not life. And nearing the farther shore we strain through scented night winds, breathless, eyes widened for the expected light. . . .

THE LUTE GIRL

by PO CHÜ-I

From the translation by L. CRANMER-BYNG; *reprinted by permission of the publishers* E. P. Dutton & Co., Inc., New York City. *Illustrated by* VICTOR HELLEU *and printed by* WILLIAM A. KITTREDGE *at* The Lakeside Press, Chicago. *The paper is* LINWEAVE JAPAN, IVORY, ANTIQUE FINISH.

Linweave Limited Editions 1931

THE LUTE GIRL

BY night, beside the river, underneath
The flower-like maple leaves that bloom alone
In autumn's silent revels of decay,
We said farewell. The host, dismounting, sped
The parting guest whose boat rocked under him,
And when the circling stirrup-cup went round,
No light guitar, no lute, was heard again;
But on the heart aglow with wine there fell
Beneath the cold bright moon the cold adieu
Of fading friends—when suddenly beyond
The cradled waters stole the lullaby
Of some faint lute; then host forgot to go,
Guest lingered on: all, wondering at the spell,
Besought the dim enchantress to reveal
Her presence; but the music died and gave
No answer, dying. Then a boat shot forth
To bring the shy musician to the shore.
Cups were refilled and lanterns trimmed again,
And so the festival went on. At last,
Slow yielding to their prayers, the stranger came,
Hiding her burning face behind her lute;
And twice her hand essayed the strings, and twice
She faltered in her task; then tenderly,
As for an old sad tale of hopeless years,
With drooping head and fingers deft she poured
Her soul forth into melodies. Now slow
The plectrum led to prayer the cloistered chords,
Now loudly with the crash of falling rain,
Now soft as the leaf whispering of words,
Now loud and soft together as the long
Patter of pearls and seed-pearls on a dish
Of marble; liquid now as from the bush
Warbles the mango bird; meandering
Now as the streamlet seawards; voiceless now
As the wild torrent in the strangling arms
Of her ice-lover, lying motionless,
Lulled in a passion far too deep for sound.
Then as the water from the broken vase
Gushes, or on the mailed horseman falls
The anvil din of steel, as on the silk
The slash of rending, so upon the strings
Her plectrum fell . . . .
        Then silence over us.
No sound broke the charmed air. The autumn moon
Swam silver o'er the tide, as with a sigh
The stranger stirred to go.
        "I passed," said she,
"My childhood in the capital; my home
Was near the hills. A girl of twelve, I learnt
The magic of the lute, the passionate
Blending of lute and voice that drew the souls

Of the great masters to acknowledgment;
And lovely women, envious of my face,
Bowed at the shrine in secret. The young lords
Vied for a look's approval. One brief song
Brought many costly bales. Gold ornaments
And silver pins were smashed and trodden down,
And blood-red silken skirts were stained with wine
In oft-times echoing applause. And so
I laughed my life away from year to year
While the spring breezes and the autumn moon
Caressed my careless head. Then on a day
My brother sought the battles in Kansuh;
My mother died: nights passed and mornings came,
And with them waned my beauty. Now no more
My doors were thronged; few were the cavaliers
That lingered by my side; so I became
A trader's wife, the chattel of a slave
Whose lord was gold, who, parting, little recked
Of separation and the unhonoured bride.
Since the tenth moon was full my husband went
To where the tea-fields ripen. I remained
To wander in my little lonely boat
Over the cold bright wave o' nights, and dream
Of the dead days, the haze of happy days,
And see them set again in dreams and tears."
        * * *
Already the sweet sorrows of her lute
Had moved my soul to pity; now these words
Pierced me the heart. "O lady fair," I cried,
"We are the vagrants of the world, and need
No ceremony to be friends. Last year
I left the Imperial City, banished far
To this plague-stricken spot, where desolation
Broods on from year to heavy year, nor lute
Nor love's guitar is heard. By marshy bank
Girt with tall yellow reeds and dwarf bamboos
I dwell. Night long and day no stir, no sound,
Only the lurking cuckoo's blood-stained note,
The gibbon's mournful wail. Hill songs I have,
And village pipes with their discordant twang.
But now I listen to thy lute methinks
The gods were parents to thy music. Sit
And sing to us again, while I engrave
Thy story on my tablets!" Gratefully
(For long she had been standing) the lute girl
Sat down and passed into another song,
Sad and so soft a dream, unlike the song
Of now ago. Then all her hearers wept
In sorrow unrestrained; and I the more,
Weeping until the pale chrysanthemums
Upon my darkened robe were starred with dew.

The Lute Girl BY VICTOR HELLEU

THE
TIGER

By William Blake

Illustrated by Theodore Ross and printed by

Carl J. H. Anderson, Franklin Printing Company, Philadelphia

The paper is Linweave Text, White

Antique Finish

LINWEAVE LIMITED EDITIONS

1931

THE
TIGER

TIGER, TIGER, BURNING BRIGHT
IN THE FORESTS OF THE NIGHT,
WHAT IMMORTAL HAND OR EYE
COULD FRAME THY FEARFUL SYMMETRY?

IN WHAT DISTANT DEEPS OR SKIES
BURNT THE FIRE OF THINE EYES?
ON WHAT WINGS DARE HE ASPIRE?
WHAT THE HAND DARE *SEIZE* THE FIRE?

AND WHAT *SHOULDER* AND WHAT ART
COULD TWIST THE SINEWS OF THY HEART?
AND, WHEN THY HEART BEGAN TO BEAT,
WHAT DREAD HAND AND WHAT DREAD FEET?

WHAT THE HAMMER? WHAT THE CHAIN?
IN WHAT FURNACE WAS THY BRAIN?
WHAT THE ANVIL? WHAT DREAD GRASP
DARE ITS DEADLY TERRORS CLASP?

WHEN THE STARS THREW DOWN THEIR SPEARS,
AND WATER'D HEAVEN WITH THEIR TEARS,
DID HE SMILE HIS WORK TO SEE?
DID HE WHO MADE THE LAMB MAKE THEE?

TIGER, TIGER, BURNING BRIGHT
IN THE FORESTS OF THE NIGHT,
WHAT IMMORTAL HAND OR EYE
DARE FRAME THY FEARFUL SYMMETRY?

Kubla Khan

BY
SAMUEL TAYLOR COLERIDGE

Reprinted by permission of the Macmillan Company; illustrated by Uriel; printed by the Rogers-Kellogg-Stillson Company in New York. The illustration is reproduced on Linweave Oxford, White, Vellum Finish; the type on Linweave Milano, Peachbeige.

LINWEAVE LIMITED EDITIONS 1931

Kubla Khan

In Xanadu did Kubla Khan
   A stately pleasure-dome decree:
Where Alph, the sacred river, ran
Through caverns measureless to man
   Down to a sunless sea.
So twice five miles of fertile ground
   With walls and towers were girdled round:
And there were gardens bright with sinuous rills
Where blossom'd many an incense-bearing tree;
And here were forests ancient as the hills,
Enfolding sunny spots of greenery.

But oh! that deep romantic chasm which slanted
Down the green hill athwart a cedarn cover!
A savage place! as holy and enchanted
As e'er beneath a waning moon was haunted
By woman wailing for her demon-lover!
And from this chasm, with ceaseless turmoil seething,
As if this earth in fast thick pants were breathing,
A mighty fountain momently was forced:
Amid whose swift half-intermitted burst
Huge fragments vaulted like rebounding hail,
Or chaffy grain beneath the thresher's flail:
And 'mid these dancing rocks at once and ever
It flung up momently the sacred river.
Five miles meandering with a mazy motion
Through wood and dale the sacred river ran,
Then reach'd the caverns measureless to man,

And sank in tumult to a lifeless ocean:
And 'mid this tumult Kubla heard from far
Ancestral voices prophesying war!

   The shadow of the dome of pleasure
      Floated midway on the waves;
   Where was heard the mingled measure
      From the fountain and the caves.
It was a miracle of rare device,
A sunny pleasure-dome with caves of ice!

   A damsel with a dulcimer
      In a vision once I saw:
   It was an Abyssinian maid,
      And on her dulcimer she play'd,
   Singing of Mount Abora.
   Could I revive within me
      Her symphony and song,
To such a deep delight 'twould win me,
That with music loud and long,
I would build that dome in air,
That sunny dome! those caves of ice!
And all who heard should see them there,
And all should cry, Beware! Beware!
His flashing eyes, his floating hair!
Weave a circle round him thrice,
   And close your eyes with holy dread,
   For he on honey-dew hath fed,
And drunk the milk of Paradise.

After Blenheim

By ROBERT SOUTHEY

ILLUSTRATED WITH A PHOTOGRAPH BY PAUL
HESSE AND PRINTED BY NORMAN T. A. MUNDER
& CO., AT BALTIMORE, MARYLAND. THE PAPER
IS LINWEAVE TEXT, IVORY, PLATE FINISH

LINWEAVE LIMITED EDITIONS
MCMXXXI

After Blenheim

IT was a summer evening,
  Old Kaspar's work was done,
And he before his cottage door
  Was sitting in the sun;
And by him sported on the green
His little grandchild, Wilhelmine.

She saw her brother Peterkin
  Roll something large and round
Which he beside the rivulet
  In playing there had found;
He came to ask what he had found
That was so large and smooth and round.

Old Kaspar took it from the boy
  Who stood expectant by;
And then the old man shook his head,
  And with a natural sigh,
"'Tis some poor fellow's skull," said he,
"Who fell in the great victory.

"I find them in the garden,
  For there's many here about;
And often when I go to plough
  The ploughshare turns them out.
For many thousand men," said he,
"Were slain in that great victory."

"Now tell us what 'twas all about,"
  Young Peterkin he cries;
And little Wilhelmine looks up
  With wonder-waiting eyes;
"Now tell us all about the war,
And what they fought each other for."

"It was the English," Kaspar cried,
  "Who put the French to rout;
But what they fought each other for
I could not well make out.
But everybody said," quoth he,
"That 'twas a famous victory.

"My father lived at Blenheim then,
  Yon little stream hard by;
They burnt his dwelling to the ground,
  And he was forced to fly.
So with his wife and child he fled,
Nor had he where to rest his head.

"With fire and sword the country round
  Was wasted far and wide
And many a childling mother then
  And newborn baby died.
But things like that, you know, must be,
At every famous victory.

"They say it was a shocking sight
  After the field was won;
For many thousand bodies here
  Lay rotting in the sun.
But things like that, you know, must be
After a famous victory.

"Great praise the Duke of Marlbro' won
  And our good Prince Eugene."
"Why 'twas a very wicked thing!"
  Said little Wilhelmine.
"Nay .. nay .. my little girl," quoth he,
"It was a famous victory.

"And everybody praised the Duke
  Who this great fight did win."
"But what good came of it at last?"
  Quoth little Peterkin.
"Why that I cannot tell," said he,
"But 'twas a famous victory."

"'Tis some poor fellow's skull," said he,
"Who fell in the great victory."

Abou Ben Adhem
by
Leigh Hunt

The illustrator, Jack Perkins;
the decorative design, Catharine
Mellen; the type face, Civilité;
the printer, The Aldus Printers,
New York; the paper, Linweave
Japan, White, Antique Finish

Linweave Limited Editions
1931

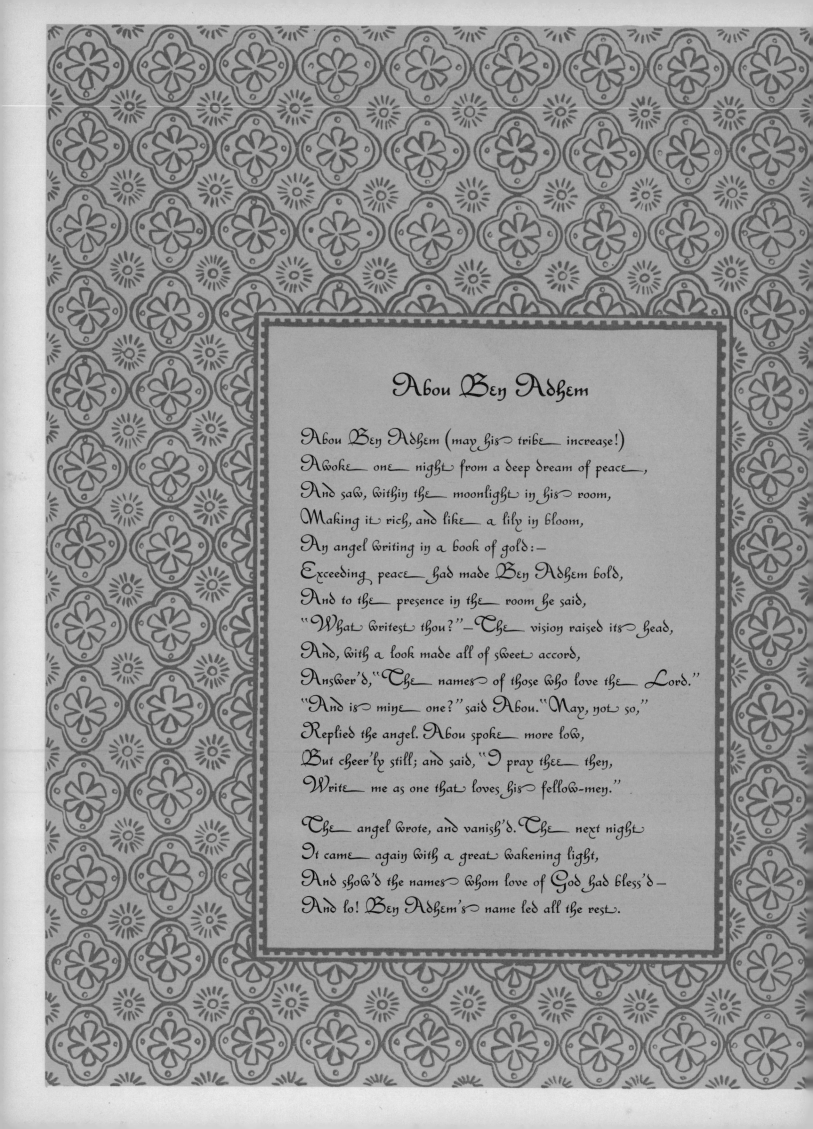

Abou Ben Adhem

Abou Ben Adhem (may his tribe increase!)
Awoke one night from a deep dream of peace,
And saw, within the moonlight in his room,
Making it rich, and like a lily in bloom,
An angel writing in a book of gold:—
Exceeding peace had made Ben Adhem bold,
And to the presence in the room he said,
"What writest thou?"—The vision raised its head,
And, with a look made all of sweet accord,
Answer'd, "The names of those who love the Lord."
"And is mine one?" said Abou. "Nay, not so,"
Replied the angel. Abou spoke more low,
But cheer'ly still; and said, "I pray thee then,
Write me as one that loves his fellow-men."

The angel wrote, and vanish'd. The next night
It came again with a great wakening light,
And show'd the names whom love of God had bless'd—
And lo! Ben Adhem's name led all the rest.

TO HELEN

BY EDGAR ALLAN POE

ILLUSTRATED BY CAROLYN EDMUNDSON

PRINTED BY CARL PURINGTON ROLLINS

AT THE PRINTING-OFFICE OF

THE YALE UNIVERSITY PRESS

ON LINWEAVE JAPAN WHITE

HALFTONE FINISH

LINWEAVE LIMITED EDITIONS

1931

TO HELEN

I SAW thee once — once only — years ago:
I must not say *how* many — but *not* many.
It was a July midnight; and from out
A full-orbed moon, that, like thine own soul, soaring,
Sought a precipitate pathway up through heaven,
There fell a silvery-silken veil of light,
With quietude, and sultriness, and slumber,
Upon the upturn'd faces of a thousand
Roses that grew in an enchanted garden,
Where no wind dared to stir, unless on tiptoe —
Fell on the upturn'd faces of these roses
That gave out, in return for the love-light,
Their odorous souls in an ecstatic death —

Fell on the upturn'd faces of these roses
That smiled and died in this parterre, enchanted
By thee, and by the poetry of thy presence.

Clad all in white, upon a violet bank
I saw thee half reclining; while the moon
Fell on the upturn'd faces of the roses,
And on thine own, upturn'd — alas, in sorrow!

Was it not Fate, that, on this July midnight —
Was it not Fate (whose name is also Sorrow)
That bade me pause before that garden-gate,
To breathe the incense of those slumbering roses?
No footstep stirred: the hated world all slept,
Save only thee and me. (Oh, Heaven! — oh, God!
How my heart beats in coupling those two words!)
Save only thee and me. I paused — I looked —
And in an instant all things disappeared.
(Ah, bear in mind this garden was enchanted!)
The pearly lustre of the moon went out:
The mossy banks and the meandering paths,
The happy flowers and the repining trees,
Were seen no more: the very roses' odors
Died in the arms of the adoring airs.
All — all expired save thee — save less than thou:
Save only the divine light in thine eyes —
Save but the soul in thine uplifted eyes.
I saw but them — they were the world to me.
I saw but them — saw only them for hours —
Saw only them until the moon went down.
What wild heart-histories seemed to lie enwritten
Upon those crystalline, celestial spheres!

How dark a woe! yet how sublime a hope!
How silently serene a sea of pride!
How daring an ambition! yet how deep —
How fathomless a capacity for love!

But now, at length, dear Dian sank from sight,
Into a western couch of thunder-cloud;
And thou, a ghost, amid the entombing trees
Didst glide away. *Only thine eyes remained.*
They *would not* go — they never yet have gone.
Lighting my lonely pathway home that night,
They have not left me (as my hopes have) since.
They follow me — they lead me through the years.
They are my ministers — yet I their slave.
Their office is to illumine and enkindle —
My duty, *to be saved* by their bright light,
And purified in their electric fire,
And sanctified in their elysian fire.
They fill my soul with Beauty (which is Hope),
And are far up in Heaven — the stars I kneel to
In the sad, silent watches of my night;
While even in the meridian glare of day
I see them still — two sweetly scintillant
Venuses, unextinguished by the sun!

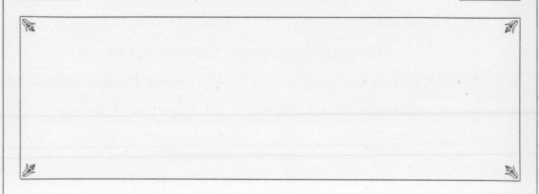

NON SUM QUALIS ERAM BONAE

SUB REGNO CYNARAE

By Ernest Dowson

Reprinted by permission of Dodd, Mead & Company, Inc.

Illustrated by Jefferson Clark; designed and

printed by Fred Anthoensen at The Southworth Press, Portland, Maine

The paper is Linweave Text, white, wove antique

Linweave Limited Editions

1931

Last night, ah, yesternight, betwixt her lips and mine
There fell thy shadow, Cynara! thy breath was shed
Upon my soul between the kisses and the wine;
And I was desolate and sick of an old passion,
    Yea, I was desolate and bowed my head:
I have been faithful to thee, Cynara! in my fashion.

All night upon mine heart I felt her warm heart beat,
Night-long within mine arms in love and sleep she lay;
Surely the kisses of her bought red mouth were sweet;
But I was desolate and sick of an old passion,
    When I awoke and found the dawn was gray:
I have been faithful to thee, Cynara! in my fashion.

I have forgot much, Cynara! gone with the wind,
Flung roses, roses riotously with the throng,
Dancing, to put thy pale, lost lilies out of mind;
But I was desolate and sick of an old passion,
    Yea, all the time, because the dance was long:
I have been faithful to thee, Cynara! in my fashion.

I cried for madder music and for stronger wine,
But when the feast is finished and the lamps expire,
Then falls thy shadow, Cynara! the night is thine;
And I am desolate and sick of an old passion,
    Yea, hungry for the lips of my desire:
I have been faithful to thee, Cynara! in my fashion.

THE CONGO

BY VACHEL LINDSAY

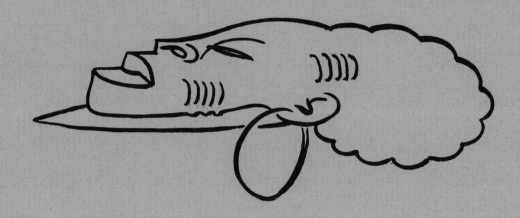

Reprinted by permission of The Macmillan Company, publishers; illustrated by Alexander King; printed in Mount Vernon at the press of William Edwin Rudge, whose type selection is the Metro series, designed by W. A. Dwiggins. The paper is Linweave Text, Sun Tan, Antique Finish.

LINWEAVE LIMITED EDITIONS 1931

THE CONGO
(A STUDY OF THE NEGRO RACE)

1. Their Basic Savagery

Fat black bucks in a wine-barrel room,
Barrel-house kings, with feet unstable,
Sagged and reeled and pounded on the table,
Pounded on the table,
Beat an empty barrel with the handle of a broom,
Hard as they were able,
Boom, boom, BOOM,
With a silk umbrella and the handle of a broom,
Boomlay, boomlay, boomlay, BOOM.

A deep rolling bass.

THEN I had religion, THEN I had a vision.
I could not turn from their revel in derision.
THEN I SAW THE CONGO, CREEPING THROUGH THE BLACK,   *More deliberate.*
CUTTING THROUGH THE JUNGLE WITH A GOLDEN TRACK.   *Solemnly chanted.*
Then along that river bank
A thousand miles
Tattooed cannibals danced in files;
Then I heard the boom of the blood-lust song
And a thigh-bone beating on a tin-pan gong.
And "BLOOD" screamed the whistles and the fifes of the warriors,   *A rapidly piling climax*
"BLOOD" screamed the skull-faced, lean witch-doctors,   *of speed and racket.*
"Whirl ye the deadly voodoo rattle,
Harry the uplands,
Steal all the cattle,
Rattle-rattle, rattle-rattle,
Bing!
Boomlay, boomlay, boomlay, BOOM,"
A roaring, epic, rag-time tune   *With a philosophic pause.*
From the mouth of the Congo
To the Mountains of the Moon.
Death is an Elephant,
Torch-eyed and horrible,   *Shrilly and with a heavily*
Foam-flanked and terrible.   *accented meter.*
BOOM, steal the pigmies,
BOOM, kill the Arabs,
BOOM, kill the white men,
HOO, HOO, HOO.
Listen to the yell of Leopold's ghost   *Like the wind in the*
Burning in Hell for his hand-maimed host.   *chimney.*
Hear how the demons chuckle and yell
Cutting his hands off down in Hell.
Listen to the creepy proclamation,
Blown through the lairs of the forest-nation,
Blown past the white-ants' hill of clay,
Blown past the marsh where the butterflies play:
"Be careful what you do,
Or Mumbo-Jumbo, God of the Congo,   *All the o sounds very golden.*
And all of the other   *Heavy accents very heavy.*
Gods of the Congo,   *Light accents very light.*
Mumbo-Jumbo will hoo-doo you,   *Last line whispered.*
Mumbo-Jumbo will hoo-doo you,
Mumbo-Jumbo will hoo-doo you."

2. Their Irrepressible High Spirits

Wild crap-shooters with a whoop and a call
Danced the Juba in their gambling-hall
And laughed fit to kill, and shook the town,
And guyed the policemen and laughed them down
With a boomlay, boomlay, boomlay, BOOM.
THEN I SAW THE CONGO, CREEPING THROUGH THE BLACK,
CUTTING THROUGH THE JUNGLE WITH A GOLDEN TRACK.
A negro fairyland swung into view,
A minstrel river
Where dreams come true.
The ebony palace soared on high
Through the blossoming trees to the evening sky.
The inlaid porches and casements shone
With gold and ivory and elephant-bone.
And the black crowd laughed till their sides were sore
At the baboon butler in the agate door,
And the well-known tunes of the parrot band
That trilled on the bushes of that magic land.

A troupe of skull-faced witch-men came
Through the agate doorway in suits of flame,
Yea, long-tailed coats with a gold-leaf crust
And hats that were covered with diamond-dust.
And the crowd in the court gave a whoop and a call
And danced the juba from wall to wall.
But the witch-men suddenly stilled the throng
With a stern cold glare, and a stern old song:
"Mumbo-Jumbo will hoo-doo you." . . .
Just then from the doorway, as fat as shotes,
Came the cake-walk princes in their long red coats,
Shoes with a patent leather shine,
And tall silk hats that were red as wine.
And they pranced with their butterfly partners there,
Coal-black maidens with pearls in their hair,
Knee-skirts trimmed with the jessamine sweet,
And bells on their ankles and little black feet.
And the couples railed at the chant and the frown
Of the witch-men lean, and laughed them down.
(Oh, rare was the revel, and well worth while,
That made those glowering witch-men smile.)

Rather shrill and high.

Read exactly as in first section.

Lay emphasis on the delicate ideas. Keep as light-footed as possible.

With pomposity.

With a great deliberation and ghostliness.

With overwhelming assurance, good cheer, and pomp.

With growing speed and sharply marked dance-rhythm.

The cake-walk royalty then began
To walk for a cake that was tall as a man
To the tune of "Boomlay, boomlay, BOOM,"
While the witch-men laughed with a sinister air,
And sang with the scalawags prancing there:
"Walk with care, walk with care,
Or Mumbo-Jumbo, God of the Congo,
And all of the other
Gods of the Congo,
Mumbo-Jumbo will hoo-doo you.
Beware, beware, walk with care,
Boomlay, boomlay, boomlay, boom,
Boomlay, boomlay, boomlay, boom,
Boomlay, boomlay, boomlay,
BOOM."
Oh, rare was the revel, and well worth while,
That made those glowering witch-men smile.

With a touch of negro
dialect, and as rapidly as
possible toward the end.

Slow, philosophic calm.

3. The Hope of their Religion

A good old negro in the slums of the town
Preached at a sister for her velvet gown.
Howled at a brother for his low-down ways,
His prowling, guzzling, sneak-thief days.
Beat on the Bible till he wore it out
Starting the jubilee revival shout.
And some had visions, as they stood on chairs,
And sang of Jacob, and the golden stairs,
And they all repented, a thousand strong,
From their stupor and savagery and sin and wrong
And slammed their hymn books till they shook the room
With "Glory, glory, glory,"
And "Boom, boom, BOOM."
THEN I SAW THE CONGO, CREEPING THROUGH THE BLACK,
CUTTING THROUGH THE JUNGLE WITH A GOLDEN TRACK.
And the gray sky opened like a new-rent veil
And showed the apostles with their coats of mail.
In bright white steel they were seated round
And their fire-eyes watched where the Congo wound.
And the twelve apostles, from their thrones on high,
Thrilled all the forest with their heavenly cry:
"Mumbo-Jumbo will die in the jungle;
Never again will he hoo-doo you,
Never again will he hoo-doo you."

Heavy bass. With a literal
imitation of camp-meeting
racket, and trance.

Exactly as in the first section.
Begin with terror and power,
end with joy.

Sung to the tune of
"Hark, ten thousand
harps and voices."

Then along that river-bank, a thousand miles,
The vine-snared trees fell down in files.
Pioneer angels cleared the way
For a Congo paradise, for babes at play,
For sacred capitals, for temples clean.
Gone were the skull-faced witch-men lean.
There, where the wild ghost-gods had wailed
A million boats of the angels sailed
With oars of silver, and prows of blue
And silken pennants that the sun shone through.
'Twas a land transfigured, 'twas a new creation.
Oh, a singing wind swept the negro nation
And on through the backwoods clearing flew:
"Mumbo-Jumbo is dead in the jungle.
Never again will he hoo-doo you.
Never again will he hoo-doo you."
Redeemed were the forests, the beasts and the men,
And only the vulture dared again
By the far, lone mountains of the moon
To cry, in the silence, the Congo tune:
"Mumbo-Jumbo will hoo-doo you.
Mumbo-Jumbo will hoo-doo you,
Mumbo . . . Jumbo . . . will . . . hoo-doo . . . you."

With growing deliberation
and joy.

In a rather high key—as
delicately as possible.

To the tune of "Hark, ten
thousand harps and voices."

Dying off into a penetrating,
terrified whisper.

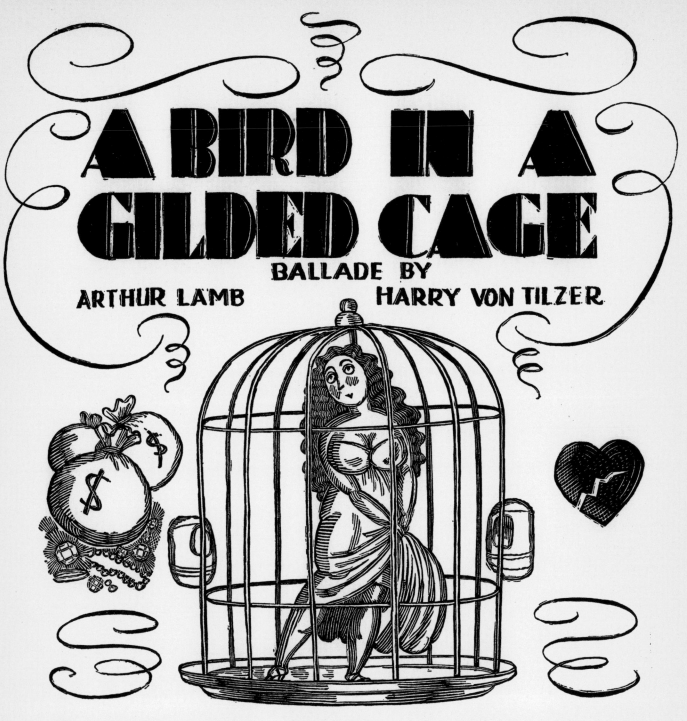

A BIRD IN A GILDED CAGE

BALLADE BY

ARTHUR LAMB   HARRY VON TILZER

THE ILLUSTRATIONS ENGRAVED BY JOHN HELD JR. IN HIS OWN INIMITABLE MANNER; THE WHOLE PRINTED WITH FEELING BY HAL MARCHBANKS AT THE MARCHBANKS PRESS. THE PAPER IS LINWEAVE ROMNEY, IVORY.
LINWEAVE LIMITED EDITIONS
—— 1931 ——

"THE BALL-ROOM WAS FILLED WITH FASHIONS THRONG, IT SHONE WITH A THOUSAND LIGHTS."

A ROMANTIC SITUATION IN THE BALLADE ENG. BY THAT FAMOUS OLD SENTIMENTALIST JOHN HELD JR WHO DANCES WITH TEARS IN HIS EYES

A Bird in a Gilded Cage

Arthur Lamb

Harry Von Tilzer

Moderato con gusto

The ball-room was filled with fash-ion's throng, It shone with a
I stood in a church-yard just at eve', When sun-set a-

thou-sand lights, ___ And there was a wo-man who passed a-long, The
dorned the West, ___ And looked at the peo-ple who'd come to grieve For

fair-est of all the sights. ___ A girl to her lov-er then soft-ly
loved ones now laid at rest. ___ A tall mar-ble mon-u-ment marked the

sighed, There's rich-es at her com-mand; ___ But she mar-ried for
grave Of one who'd been fash-ion's queen, ___ And I thought she is

wealth, not for love, he cried, Though she lives in a man-sion grand. ___
hap-pi-er here at rest, Then to have peo-ple say when seen: ___

She's on-ly a bird in a gild-ed cage, A beau-ti-ful sight to

see, ___ You may think she's hap-py and free from care, She's not, though she

seems to be, ___ 'Tis sad when you think of her was-ted life, For

youth can-not mate with age, ___ And her beau-ty was sold For an

old man's gold, She's a bird in a gild-ed cage. ___

"SHE IS HAPPIER HERE AT REST"